Red and the Moon

A Love Story in Letters

Krista S. Rose

Cover image provided by Abdul Gani M, courtesy of Unsplash.

ISBN: 978-0-9964189-5-9

10 9 8 7 6 5 4 3 2 1

Also by Krista S. Rose

SAGA OF THE ROSE

The Chosen Trilogy
Book One: Whispers of Heaven
Book Two: ShatterStar
Book Three: The Nothing Light

The Dragonwrayth Trilogy: Brannyn's Tale
Book One: Among the Ashes

The Imperium Trilogy: Lanya's Tale
Book One: The Summer Throne

The LightningMage Trilogy: Kylee's Tale
Book One: Voice of Wolves

OTHER WORKS
Red and the Moon: A Love Story in Letters
Whispers of Heaven: Illustrated Edition (coming soon)
Awakening (coming soon)
The Compendium: A Codex of Ca'erdylla (coming soon)
Worldbuilding Workbook (coming soon)

For Suzie

The most beautiful person I have ever met

I hope my legacy will honor the memory of you

Contents

Meeting

Dear Lady,

Forgive me
I wish only to tell you
That meeting you tonight
Was a beautiful happening

-M.

Kind Sir,

Thank you for your flattering note
I worried so that you found me foolish
I am unused to strangers and lords
Please forgive me if I offend

-R.

Dearest Lady,

You could not offend, your honesty is lovely
And you could never be foolish
For the gods create no foolish angels
I wish no longer to be a stranger, but a friend

-M.

My friend,

Your letters are the joys of my days
But I admit a certain curiosity
Why you should converse with a simple peasant girl
When you are a nobleman's son

-R.

Romance

Lovely Angel,

You ask why I converse with you
Honesty then
When I saw your face the night we met
Your eyes filled with stars
The moonlight stroking your cheek
Ah, how I longed to be the moon!

Your lips were red as rubies
They still fill the quiet places of my mind
I find myself staring at all that is red around me
You fill my every thought

Forgive me, gentle angel
But I fear my heart is no longer my own
It was stolen away by you
When I saw your face that night

-The Moon

Sweet Moon,

Your letter fills my trembling heart
I run my fingers over your words
As I stare up at the brilliant moon and wonder
Do you feel its light as I do, warm upon skin?

The night draws in softly around me
As quiet as your smile
The stars tempt me with thoughts of your shy eyes
As tender as the moonlight now touching my face

If I have stolen your heart, then it is only fair
For mine no longer beats for me
It is only under the moon that I feel alive
As I was when I gazed upon you

-Red

Beautiful Red,

My chest aches with every breath
My arms are heavy from emptiness
All the stars are a thousand times too bright
The moon that can touch your skin mocks me

You are too far from me
I beg of you to let me see you again
To witness the sparkle of starlight upon your hair
To see the cruel moon caress your cheek

Forgive me my desperation, my desire
Your smile is the sweetest wine
I cannot help wanting to drink my fill
To spend all my days and nights drunk on you

-The Moon

Sweet Moon,

I whisper your name in my prayers
And beg the gods to see your face again
Such short meetings between us are a torment
I fear they will be the death of me

-Red

Beautiful Red,

My heart is filled with such a fire
I will surely burn before you see me again
If I am consumed by this inferno known as love
Take my ashes so that I might at last be close to you

-The Moon

Sweet Moon,

Such a strange thing, this love
To long to be with another person for eternity
Love is the closest we shall come to immortality
For surely such a love can never truly die

-Red

Proposal

Beautiful Red,

I can no longer live with stolen moments
The brush of my fingers against your silks
Your sidelong glances
The soft fall of your hair against your ivory neck
I am in flames
My will is ashes beneath your feet

What foolishness to hide what we feel
When our love burns so brightly it dims the very sun
Ah, my crimson angel, what a spell I'm under!
My very soul aches for you

I beg you to accept my humble heart
Take my hand, my name, my soul
You shall be my queen, my world
And I, your moon, to brighten your darkest night

-The Moon

Sweet Moon,

Your words echo the desires of my heart
But though I long to take all you offer
I am yet afraid of your father's anger
Perhaps we should wait, just a while longer

-Red

Beautiful Red,

Too long now have we waited out of fear
I am more than my title, more than my inheritance
If we are immortal in this love
Then it is not my father's hand I wish to hold through eternity

-The Moon

Sweet Moon,

I can hold out against you no longer
Come, take my hand, and my soul
All I am is yours
If you would have me

-Red

Announcement

Beautiful Red,

Your tears break me
I beg you, speak to me
I do not know what to do

-The Moon

Sweet Moon,

Surely I cannot be worth your father's disownment
You should not lose everything for me

-Red

Beautiful Red,

You are everything

-The Moon

Engagement

Sweet Moon,

Your words soothe me
Though I am still afraid
Your father's words linger in my ears
What if our love cannot sustain us?

-Red

Beautiful Red,

I do not care what my father said
Do not listen to his echoes
Poverty with you will be heaven
My title is only a gilded cage alone

I know I have promised you the finest things
I swear now before all the gods
I will still give them to you
I will lay the world at your feet

-The Moon

Sweet Moon,

I need no golden goblets, no silver rings
All I need is in your eyes
What need have I of the world
When I have the moon?

-Red

Wedding

Sweet Moon,

Is it a dream
Can any of this be real
Your father gave us his blessing
I am nearly afraid to sleep

-Red

Beautiful Red,

It is almost more than I can believe
After tomorrow I will never again be without you

-The Moon

Sweet Moon,

My love for you is all that keeps me strong
I grow sick of fabrics and jewels
The chattering of the crowds
This parade of glittering

Weddings are truly ridiculous things
But I comfort myself with the sight of you

-Red

Love

Beautiful Red,

You look so radiant
Sleeping atop the red silks of our bed

I have drawn all the curtains
I am the only one who shall ever see you like this
I will not share you
Not even with the moonlight

-The Moon

Sweet Moon,

The night is quiet all around us
Though I swore I heard thunder beneath your hands
These last few days have been a beautiful awakening
More lovely than any imagining

My skin yet burns where you kissed me
My lips taste of sweetness and fire
The moon peeks into our room through the curtains
Sliding silver-white over your skin

I marvel at you sleeping, full of wonder
All my foolish, girlish dreams
Are made real and whole and beautiful
By the magic that is you

-Red

Beautiful Red,

I watch you in the garden
Your hands full of flowers
The lovely line of your throat
Begs for my lips

How many times have I loved you
In how many lifetimes
And yet I am crushed by this wanting
I collapse, helpless, at your delicate feet

I shall tie you to the bed, my love
And tie myself to you with crimson ties
That we shall simply stay in paradise forever
And no more wander aching from it

-The Moon

Sweet Moon,

This fire that consumes us
I fear burns too brightly
What could be left of this love
When all at last fades to ashes?

-Red

Beautiful Red,

We are immortal in our love
And I have always and only loved you

-The Moon

Arguments

Beautiful Red,

Do not be angered with me, my love
I did not mean to spill the wine on your new dress
It is only that I craved something far sweeter

-The Moon

Sweet Moon,

If I did not love you quite so much
I might be tempted to throw this quill at your head

-Red

Beautiful Red,

Ah, you anger so!
Glorious in your passionate rage
I long to kiss those ruby lips
And feel the fire in your eyes burn me

-The Moon

Sweet Moon,

Forgive me for forgetting our meal
I should not have grown distracted in the garden
I fear we shall always be haunted
By the scent of smoke

-Red

Beautiful Red,

I am not angry, my love
It was only that I did not want to laugh
When your eyes were full of tears
It was I who distracted you in the garden, after all

I would gladly burn a thousand meals
If it meant sating your hunger

-The Moon

Children

Beautiful Red,

If you were not carrying our child
I would bring you with me on these journeys
The laws of the lords be damned

-The Moon

Sweet Moon,

I understand your responsibilities
Yet these selfish desires compel me to protest
I wish you could forget the business of lords
So that you could stay always beside me

-Red

Beautiful Red,

If it were not for the legacy
I want to leave our child
I would ignore these summons of duty
And not even the gods could drag me from your side

-The Moon

Sweet Moon,

I felt the surge of our child today
As it moved beneath my heart
And I was filled with an unknown wonder
Ah, my love, the joys you show me!

Hurry home to me, do not linger
These laws of lords mean little to us
Who after all can rule the happiness of our hearts?
What king or angel can challenge the moon?

-Red

Beautiful Red,

I sit here quiet and full of wonder
Watching as you nurse our son
I fear for once my words are insufficient
To describe the joy that fills my being

You are a glorious angel, dressed in white silk
Your hair gleams with the flickering of the flames
Your eyes as you lift them to mine
Are full of stars and mysteries

Ah, divine goddess of beauty
I am blessed with your most wondrous creation
She is a creature of dreams and passion
I fear my heart shall burst from love

-The Moon

War

Sweet Moon,

What do I care for kings and crowns?
What faceless names demand our lives?
Demand that blood be spilled on virgin stones?
Oh, love, my heart is sick with fear for you

-Red

Beautiful Red,

I have always considered myself a patriot
But now as I march toward impending war
My only thought is of returning to you
I fear these miles shall make me a traitor

-The Moon

Sweet Moon,

Tonight I left the children in their beds
And walked in our gardens, dark and cold
The long, gentle days of summer are lost
Will this endless winter never cease?

I am tormented by dreams and shadows
A thousand memories of you in every corner of our house
In every corner of my mind
I beg the moon to show me your face
I beg the gods to keep you safe

Come home again, my love, to me

-Red

Beautiful Red,

How I long to be with you again
Away from the senseless stench of death
To hold our children once more
And walk with you in the gardens

My mind is always full of you
Everywhere is the color red
But it is harsh and ugly
A mocking reminder of your sweetness

My heart aches to be home with you
Where I will love you endlessly
I shall hold you for a lifetime, my love
And never again let you go

-The Moon

Sweet Moon,

Surely the kings must be sick of blood
That turns the rivers and seas to black
I am afraid that you too shall return a ghost
A shade such as the soldiers in town

Remember me, my love
Keep safe my heart, which you carry with you
Until at last you are returned to me
I will never let you go again

-Red

Beautiful Red,

How you guide me through the darkness!
How you save me from myself!
These shadows are a hated enemy
Yet you defeat them so easily

My hands are stained with blood
But you wash me clean
How can I claim to be your moon
When it is you who are the light in my darkness?

-The Moon

Sweet Moon,

They say the war is almost over
And my heart begs for it to be true
My tears fall now in constant rains
Your scent haunts me in my sleep

How much longer must you be gone?
It grows harder to breathe without you

-Red

Beautiful Red,

I shall be home soon, my love
I will wrap myself in your red silks
And tie myself to you once again
I shall remain with you this time for eternity

-The Moon

Post-War

Beautiful Red

I fear you are a dream
I am nearly afraid to sleep
I shall wake
And be returned to the war

-The Moon

Sweet Moon,

Your screams of terror woke me
What a terrible thing is war
Even after, it yet haunts you
As if the blood were still upon your hands

Now I watch you sleep, peaceful again
Your ghosts haunt me instead
Ah, sweet prince, what terrors you have seen!
And yet your hands remain so gentle

Your love is tender, but I sense desperation
Do not fear, my silver light
For you are safe in my arms once more
And none shall ever take you from me again

-Red

home

Beautiful Red,

The house is quiet and peaceful
But I ache even in this brief emptiness
How is it possible to love one person so much
Where even an hour's separation is agony?

Your face is unchanged by these ten years
Since first I saw you beneath the stars
My love is a vast ocean
For you, I willingly drown

Gods, give me the strength
Not to crawl to you on my knees
Not to beg you to never again leave me here alone
Not even for a single hour

-The Moon

Sweet Moon,

You are my soul, my light, my world
And I say this with all the love burning in my heart
Stop stealing my pies from the kitchen
Or I will scold you like the children

-Red

Beautiful Red,

You are the most frustrating angel
Must you put everything where I cannot find it?

-The Moon

Sweet Moon,

Today we stole a golden moment
You held my hand in perfect quiet
As the moon slowly rose, our guardian
My life is so much sweeter for your light

The moon touched my face as you kissed my fingertips
Do you remember that day when we met?
It seems only moments have passed
And yet I have always and only loved you

-Red

Sickness

Beautiful Red,

The doctors tell me not to hover
But I am bound to your side with chains of fear
How can I rest when this fever that has taken your voice
Threatens to take everything else I hold dear?

I have seen darkness before, my love
But nothing compares to this terror
There is no enemy to fight, no blood I can spill
I have never felt so helpless

It seems I have spent a thousand nights in prayers
Gentle gods, protect our love
I fear not death, nor heaven, nor hell
But the loss of my soul, my love, my light

-The Moon

Sweet Moon,

You have not left me in days, my love
If you will not sleep
I must ask that you at least eat
The moon should not be quite so pale

-Red

Beautiful Red,

Even in the throes of this deathly illness
You think only of me
But I must ask, my darling angel
That you think first of your health

-The Moon

Sweet Moon,

You are finally sleeping
Your face looks drawn in the firelight
These last few weeks have aged us
When did so much silver appear in our hair?

This dreadful weakness in my limbs
I cannot even stand
But my love for you is stronger still
I can endure anything with you by my side

-Red

Beautiful Red,

I dreamed that you were taken from me
And all the lights in the world were put out
I stumbled through the darkness alone
Please, my love, do not leave me here

-The Moon

Sweet Moon,

They say I am past the worst of it
But I still feel so weak
I am shamed that I look so in front of you
Please stop staring

-Red

Beautiful Red,

Forgive me, my love, I cannot help myself
You are the most beautiful thing I have ever seen

-The Moon

Children
Leaving

Sweet Moon,

We spent a lovely hour in the garden today
And watched as our children played
They are almost grown, my love
My heart aches for their inevitable leaving

-Red

Beautiful Red,

It is the duty of sons
To outgrow their fathers
Ours is a man now, and I have never been so proud
He bears our legacy with your grace

-The Moon

Sweet Moon,

It is our son's wedding day

I fear my heart is broken
I wish he was a small child again
That I could wrap him in my arms
And never let him go

-Red

Beautiful Red,

Do not cry so
My heart drowns in your tears
I would suffer through any war again
Not to feel your heartbreak

-The Moon

Krista S. Rose

Sweet Moon,

These tears are not sadness
They are joy
Our true legacy was not our titles or our lands
But the love that we passed on to our children

It is this that sets me to weeping
For our love has burned brighter than any sun
That it could light up our daughter's eyes
And fill the smile of our first grandchild

Ah, my love, the joys you show me!
I fear for once my words are insufficient
One heart is not enough for this happiness
One lifetime is not enough for this love

-Red

Old Age

Krista S. Rose

Sweet Moon,

My hair is silver now, my hands grow frail
And yet when you look at me
I am seventeen again, beautiful and fair
Your lips still make me tremble

How strange is love!
One lifetime is not enough for this fire
Will the gods unite us in the next that we might burn on?
It would be cruel to exist without you

-Red

Beautiful Red,

Do not fear the encroaching darkness
The gods are kind and gracious
Love this strong cannot die with fragile bodies
I will be yours through every lifetime to come

-The Moon

Sweet Moon,

Are we immortal in our love?
For I have always and only loved you

-Red

Death

Beautiful Red,

Cruel fate has taken you before me
To suffer alone in this lightless world
Wait for me, my love, my crimson angel
I follow you now to the next beautiful adventure

-The Moon

Acknowledgements

A huge thank you to my family and friends that have supported my writing all these years. This book is for you.

Special mention to Evi, who read every draft of this without complaint; Violet, who said the words I needed to hear; Tylo, whose honest opinion I value above all others; and my mom, who encourages me in all that I do. Your support means the world to me.

About the Author

Krista S. Rose has always been fascinated by fantasy, and has been building the world of Ca'erdylla for over twenty years. The stories, which began as a game with her brothers and sisters, have grown to become an obsession, competing with her love of video games, books, and Italian food.

Krista hopes you enjoyed *Red and the Moon,* and invites you to read her books in the Saga of the Rose series, now available in paperback and kindle on Amazon.

Feel free to contact Krista! She loves to hear from you!
Facebook: www.facebook.com/catnamedsnowball
Email: kristasrose@yahoo.com

Made in the USA
Las Vegas, NV
13 October 2021

32231777R00069